MY HOLIDAY
DRAWING
BOOK

by Gillian Johnson

ACKNOWLEDGEMENTS

Publishing Director   Piers Pickard
Art Director   Andy Mansfield
Commissioning Editors   Jen Feroze,
                             Catharine Robertson
Author and illustrator   Gillian Johnson
Editor   Jacqueline McCann
Print Production   Larissa Frost,
                             Nigel Longuet

Published in April 2018 by Lonely Planet Global Limited
CRN 554153
ISBN 978 1 78701 316 2
www.lonelyplanetkids.com
© Lonely Planet 2018

10 9 8 7 6 5 4 3 2 1

Printed in China

Lonely Planet Offices

Australia
The Malt Store, Level 3, 551 Swanston St, Carlton,
Victoria 3053
T: 03 8379 8000

Ireland
Digital Depot, Roe Lane (off Thomas St), Digital Hub, Dublin 8,
D08 TCV4

USA
124 Linden St, Oakland, CA 94607
T: 510 250 6400

UK
240 Blackfriars Rd, London SE1 8NW
T: 020 3771 5100

STAY IN TOUCH
lonelyplanet.com/contact

MY HOLIDAY
DRAWING
BOOK

CALLING
ALL
TRAVELLERS!

There is no right way to draw - everyone has their own style, and one person's mistake is another person's masterpiece. Follow our easy tips and you'll come home with a book packed with sketches and doodles that will help you relive your amazing holiday.

MY HOLIDAY

Let's start with you – that's a good place! Where are you going? Who's going with you? Fill in the empty boxes with words, doodles, drawings and whatever you feel like.

This is me!

Where I live...

Where I'm going...

Who's going with me...

How I'll get there...

Most looking forward to...

WHAT YOU NEED

Wherever you find yourself, you'll need a few drawing tools such as pencils, markers, crayons or pastels. A water soluble pen is great for smearing, blending and creating special effects. A rubber and pencil sharpener are also useful. Keep all your pens together in a pencil case and store it in your rucksack for easy access. You're all set!

HERE'S WHAT TO BRING...

two pencils, h
and soft lea

a rubber

two or three
water soluble
coloured pencils

a selection of pens (rollerball,
marker, colouring pen)

colour pastels or crayons

a pencil sharpener

WARM UP

You don't need to be an art ace to draw what you see, just be prepared to have fun on the page. With a few pens, pencils, a rubber and some water, you can create amazing effects. Choose your pen and see what it can do. Don't worry about being messy – it's important to experiment!

Lines

Lines can be long, short, straight, wiggly, thick or thin.

Take a line for a walk...

Continue these patterns across the space.

Scribbles

Scribbles don't have to have any structure at all. Just let loose!

Smudging

Dip your finger in water to smudge and blur pen and pencil lines.

LET GO

Fill this page with balloons! Who was holding them before they escaped?

WHERE TO?

Where are you going? Write the names of the places you'll visit on your journey on the signpost.

Decorate the sign **HoWEvER** you like! Try a mix of **CAPITAL** And lower case Letters and use different **colours.**

Draw a map showing how you get to your destination. Use your imagination
and show some of the things you might pass along the way.

TOP TIP

Make a map key. You could
include features such as a
house, town, lake, forest,
mountain, railway station,
airport, hospital and school.
Can you think of others?

BUBBLE LETTERS

All packed? Make sure your suitcase or rucksack has your name on it. Create your own personalized tag and draw a baggage label using bubble letters.

NAME

ADDRESS

COUNTRY

TELEPHONE

STICK PEOPLE

Who is going with you? Your mum, dad, sister or brother? Classmates on a school trip? Try to capture them as stick people. They work best if their actions seem real. Group a few stick people together and before you know it, you'll have a story.

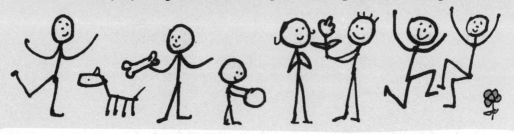

Draw some happy stick figures. Try to make the head and body the same length as the legs.

Draw sad stick figures. Think about the angles of the body and head to put across the emotions.

Sketch angry stick figures! The elbows come halfway down the arms and point backwards. Knees are halfway down the legs and point forwards.

Now draw exhausted stick figures and see if you can copy the angles of their poses.

MY STICK FAMILY PORTRAIT

Test your stick-drawing technique by applying it to your own family. Try to capture your family when they are hanging around. Use speech bubbles to add funny comments!

It's your turn! Maybe you're at an airport, or train station, or about to board a ferry? See if you can recreate the scene using simple stick people and speech bubbles. Add a caption too.

TAKE A CLOSE LOOK

Many of the objects that you see around you can be broken down into simple shapes. Most objects can be broken down into a sphere, cube or cylinder – the building blocks of drawing. Whenever you draw, it helps to look for these basic shapes.

sphere   cube   cylinder

Adding little lines with a fine pen will help to make objects appear 3-D.

With a pencil, you can create a soft shadow.

Practise drawing these shapes. Then, using a fine black pen, add lines to create a 3-D appearance. Finally, use your pencil to add shading and depth.

... EVEN CLOSER

The cube, sphere and cylinder form the basic shape for all sorts of everyday objects, and even people. Learn to look for these shapes.

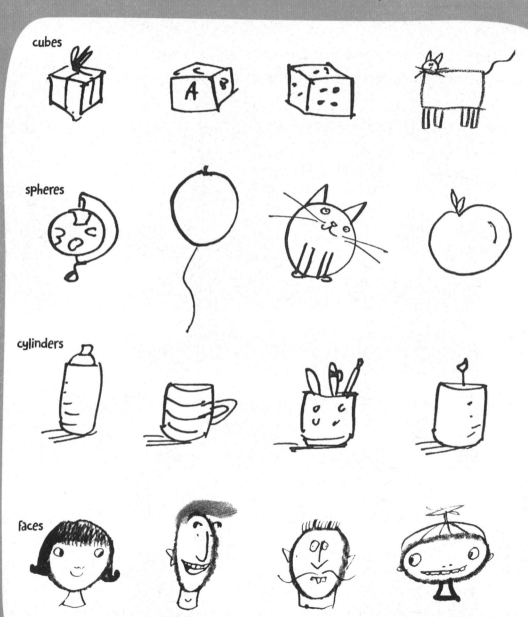

cubes

spheres

cylinders

faces

Can you turn these shapes into everyday objects?

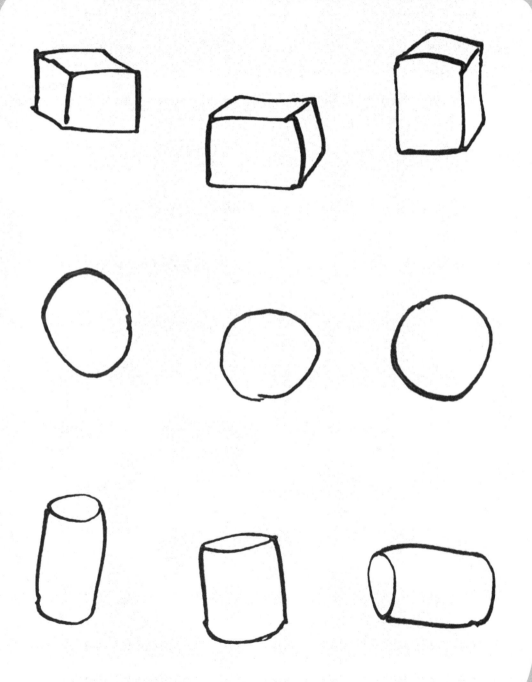

CRAZY CREATURES

Can you change these basic shapes into animals? Feel free to go a little crazy. We've done a few for you!

ON THE MOVE

Whether you're camping with a school friend, visiting Grandma on the train, or hopping on a plane to Timbuktu, you'll need a vehicle of some kind to get there. Have a go at drawing yours and remember to look out for basic shapes that make up vehicles!

THE HORIZON

The place where the land meets the sky is called the horizon. On the page, it looks like a straight line drawn across the middle. It can be high up, low down, wavy, bumpy, straight or pointed.

Draw your horizon high up. This will give you room for details in the foreground and less room for sky.

Draw two lines from the foreground to the middle of the horizon to create a road disappearing into the distance.

Add details such as mountains in the distance. Experiment with making them higher or lower.

A lower horizon line gives a bigger sky but leaves less room for foreground detail.

Now add a series of lines getting smaller and smaller to create telegraph poles.

Add a few road markings, some fluffy clouds, or W shapes for birds to the sky.

It's your turn. Experiment by drawing a horizon that is high up the page. Add a few simple details to your scene to create a landscape.

Now draw a horizon that is lower down the page.

VANISHING POINT

When something is so far away and so small, it seems to vanish. That's the vanishing point! When you're trying to add depth (called perspective) to your drawings, it helps to remember that things that are far away look much smaller than things that are close up.

A page with a horizon line, a vanishing point and dotted lines connecting the two will help you create a drawing with perspective.

The bigger buildings and trees in this picture appear closer. Smaller trees and buildings seem far away.

Now it's your turn to experiment with perspective. Draw your horizon and vanishing point and connect them with faint lines.

A

B

C

D

Try drawing simple buildings, trees or telegraph poles to create a scene with perspective.

PERSPECTIVE

Have a go at drawing people using perspective. The same rule applies: the smaller you draw them, the further away they will appear! What are your people doing?

On sports' day, you'll notice that the boy standing close to you in lane 1 looks much bigger than the boy far away in lane 10!

This lot are ready for a downhill challenge. Change a few details and positions to give the impression your people are all different.

MARK MAKING

When you add lines, flecks, specks, dots, criss-crosses and bubbles, it adds texture to your sketches and drawings.

Practise making marks here. Can you think of other marks you can make?
Think about how you can apply marks like these to your sketchings.

LIGHT & SHADE

Shadows happen when light hits the object you are drawing. To figure out how to draw shadows, imagine pointing a torch at the thing you're drawing. The shadows happen in the places the light doesn't reach.

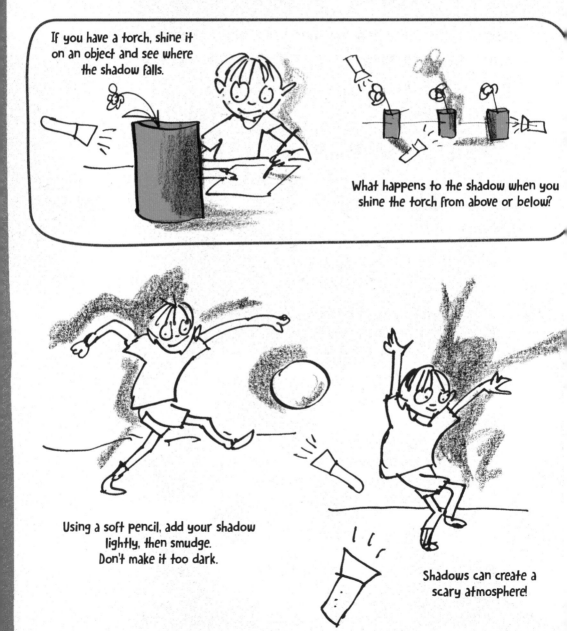

If you have a torch, shine it on an object and see where the shadow falls.

What happens to the shadow when you shine the torch from above or below?

Using a soft pencil, add your shadow lightly, then smudge. Don't make it too dark.

Shadows can create a scary atmosphere!

It's your turn. Add shadows to these sketches and think carefully about how the light from the torch will hit each one. Where will the shadows fall?

TREES AND MORE TREES

No matter where you are, it's very likely there will be trees (unless you're on the Moon). First try to capture the general shape – is it round, oval, triangular? Don't worry about adding individual leaves. Where is the light coming from? Add shadows.

oval / round

three circles

triangular

Have a go at drawing tree shapes. You could add branches – they are thicker at the base than at the tip. Then add markings and create shadows using a soft pencil.

DRAW A FOREST

Draw different tree shapes and create a forest. Add leaves at the top to make a leafy canopy. Think about basic shapes, and have a go at branches. They are like veins, getting smaller and smaller as they reach towards the sky. Let the branches curve a little too. Add markings to your tree trunks and canopy. Have fun and remember – there are no mistakes!

CONTOUR DRAWING

Contour drawing is a classic art exercise. Try not to look at your pencil or paper as you draw – so you are drawing 'blind'. Look at an object and try to imagine that your pen is almost touching the edge as you outline it (contour means 'outline' in French). Let's start with the hand. Don't peek!

Make a contour drawing while you look at your other hand. Think about the outer edges.

Look at your hand from different angles and try different poses. Try drawing with your other hand too.

You'll soon get the hang of it. The more you practise, the better your contour drawings will be.

Use this space to practise sketching your own hand.
Don't worry if it looks a bit messy to start with – that's the idea!

A IS FOR ACCOMMODATION

Where are you staying on your holiday? What's it like? Are you in a skyscraper 50 floors up? Sleeping in a campervan or a tent? Whether you're in a hotel, treehouse or at sea, try recreating the place where you are laying your head! Zzzzzzzzz

LOOK UP!

If you're in a town or a city, take a few moments to look up — what do you see? Does the skyline look different from where you live? Draw a row of tall rectangles, and then draw another row in front to create a sense of depth, or perspective.

TOP TIP

Add lots of details to your rectangles – dots, dashes or squares to look like windows. Work on your roof shapes and try to make them different.

GRAND FAÇADE

When you look closely at a skyline, individual buildings such as museums, palaces and churches may be very grand. Use a soft pencil to sketch a grand building, or your favourite building.

Use your finger to rub and smudge your image slightly.

With a fine black pen, add a few details to bring your building to life.

Try to recreate a building you have seen on your travels, or one close to where you live.

Experiment with a fine black pen and practise your mark-making skills to bring your building to life.

PEOPLE, PEOPLE, PEOPLE

It's a lot of fun watching people with a pen in one hand and a sketchbook in the other. Whether you're strolling through town, throwing a frisbee on the beach or walking in the woods, try to capture something of the people around you.

People move, so you need to work quickly! Try to capture a general shape. It might take a few people to warm up, but don't worry – you'll get better the more you do.

TOP TIP

Let loose! Dab a few fingerprints on the page and you can turn those into people, too!

DRAWING FACES

Round, oval, egg-shaped or square – heads and faces come in all shapes and sizes! Here are a few handy tips to remember when you're drawing them.

1 Draw an egg-shaped face to begin.

2 Sketch the eyes about halfway up. There should be a lot of space above the eyes.

3 The tips of the ears begin just a little above the eyes, and end halfway between the eyes and the chin.

4 The nose sits at the same level as the ends of the ears.

5 The bottom lip sits halfway between the bottom of the ear lobes and the chin. The mouth is shaped a little like a wide triangle!

Now you have a go. Try using a combination of pencils: a thick crayon or pastel for hair and a thinner black pen for details.

MOODY PEOPLE

You can create a range of moods by altering the shape of the mouth or the eyes. Varying the distance between the eyes changes someone a lot. Have a go and then write funny captions to show how they're feeling.

HATS OFF

Hats can completely change a person's appearance. Like people, each hat has its own personality. Have a little fun adding your own hats to the people here - or copy one that's around the edge of the page. Do the hats suit their wearers?

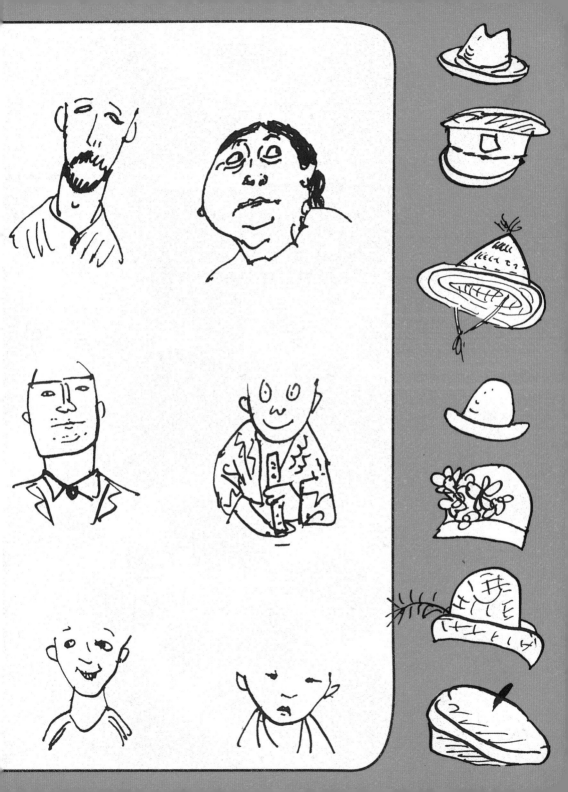

BIRDS

Take a moment to notice the different kinds of birds around you. Even if you're not in a place filled with feathered friends, this bird drill will help you to draw them anywhere!

The basic shape is the most important part of making a bird look like a bird!

A bird shape is a series of circles, ovals, triangles and cylinders.

Add details such as feathers, a pointy beak, a beady eye, scratchy feet and tail feathers.

Use this space for your bird studies.

CREATURES GREAT AND SMALL

The world is full of brilliant beasts. Lizards on walls, ants marching by the pool, dogs sleeping in the shade, horses in the field, birds in the sky or whales in the sea... See if you can outline them here - practise your contour drawing.

CREATE A MENU

One of the great things about being on holiday is that you get to try all kinds of new things and eat all sorts of treats. Create the perfect menu of all your favourite things from your trip using your best swirly lettering.

STREET SIGNS

Have you seen any interesting street signs on your journey? Lots of countries have signs that might be strange to you. Here are a few. Why not draw one you have seen, or make one up for fun!

AT THE BEACH

Head down to the beach and record what you see. Or imagine what you might see! Try to use some of the techniques you've learned so far.

PICTURE GALLERY

If you could frame the most incredible things you've done so far on your holiday, what would they be? Mountain climbing, zip wiring, swimming, playing football, riding a horse, or climbing a tree?

Or why not ask everyone to empty their pockets and draw the things that most remind you of your trip!

SAY GOODBYE

Now you know that cool things can happen on the page with a few simple techniques and a little practise. What have you enjoyed sketching most? Here's a place to show off!